I Love You 1 to 10

Written by Melissa McCann
Illustrated by Drew Keeler

ISBN: 978-1-64704-297-4 (eBook)
ISBN: 978-1-64704-298-1 (Paperback)
ISBN: 978-1-64704-299-8 (Hardcover)

For all of my sunshines

Little Fox was playing in the meadow
when he heard Mama Fox call,
"Time to come in, Sweetheart."

Little Fox came prancing back to his foxhole. For he knew at the end of the day, it was also time for some great big snuggles from Mama Fox.

"Are you ready for our count, my little fox?" Mama Fox asked as she snuggled him into their cozy little den.

"I sure am, Mama."

"Will you count with me tonight?"

"Sure, Mama, I love counting with you."

As Mama Fox started her count, Little Fox began thinking of all the fun he had that day.

"Number 1: I love you the most."

"Number 2: You are my sunshine."

"Number 3: I am your mama, and it's my favorite thing to do."

"Number 4: You are always safe with me."

Little Fox looked up at his mama and smiled,

"Number 4: I am always safe with you!"

"Number 5:" Mama Fox continued,

"We can do hard things."

"Number 6: I love the way your mind works."

"Number 7: You make me so happy."

Little Fox giggled before he said,

"Number 7: You make ME so happy!"

"Number 8: You are so kind."

"Number 9: You are so brave."

"Number 10 : I love everything about you!"

Z
Z
Z
Z
Z

As Mama Fox finished up Number 10, Little Fox yawned his last yawn of the evening.

He fell fast asleep,
dreaming of another great day.

Dear Readers,

I'm so glad this book found you! My intention was to create a really simple and enjoyable reading experience for both you and the child you are reading with. From my perspective, every child is so different, thus reading activities with any child will vary. This project was created from my own experience with my son who preferred running around in circles rather than a nightly reading session. So rather than wrestle with him every night, I began to count with him. As I counted, I told him in various ways how much I loved him. We started with 5 statements and soon got up to 10. Within a week he was much more calm at bedtime, and began to ask for "our count." Soon after, he was counting on his own and started creating his own positive phrases. He loved hearing all these special things I was telling him. The beautiful part is that it was so special for him AND for me. At the end of a long day, it was a great reminder of the relationship I was building with him.

In this time of uncertainty, I believe LOVE is so vital. . . showing love, expressing love, feeling loved. If you happen to have a rambunctious toddler like I did, or perhaps just a child who needs to hear how important they are to you, then this book is for you. Happy reading, counting, and so much loving!

Melissa McCann

CPSIA information can be obtained
at www.ICGtesting.com
Printed in the USA
LVHW071010050321
678866LV00002B/1

* 9 7 8 1 6 4 7 0 4 2 9 9 8 *